C000175280

This
SpongeBob
SquarePants
Annual
belongs to:

NICKELODEON®

SpongeBob SquarePants™

ANNUAL 2005

CONTENTS

Edited by Brenda Apsley
Designed by Craig Cameron and Graham Wise

Created by Steve Hillenburg.
Some of the material in this annual was previously published in Nickelodeon Magazine Nicktoons Specials 1, 5 and 8.

Published in Great Britain in 2004 by Egmont Books Ltd,
239 Kensington High Street, London W8 6SA.
Printed in Italy. 3 5 7 9 10 8 6 4 2 1 ISBN 1 4052 1395 7

Hi!
C'mon, let's dive right into my first ever annual!

In one of the houses in Bikini Bottom – a two-storey furnished pineapple, what else? – lives a square yellow sea sponge. His name is SpongeBob SquarePants.

SpongeBob's an innocent optimist who always looks on the bright side of things. He means well, but somehow always manages to get himself into hot water without really trying. Everywhere he goes, trouble seems to be one step behind, just waiting to trip him up.

SpongeBob's a cook at the Krusty Krab Fast Food restaurant and his only goal in life is to make the perfect Krabby Patty so that his boss will make him Employee of the Month. Every month.

the Snail

SpongeBob shares his pineapple home with his pet snail, Gary who meows like a cat.

SPONGEBOB LIKES...

- chasing wild jellyfish
- thinking about hard questions like: 'How many sardines can a school bus hold?'
- going around in his tighty whitey underpants his best friend and neighbour, Patrick Star
- Frying up Krabby Patties

SPONGEBOB DISLIKES...

Say Hi to the Gang

Patrick Star is the best friend and neighbour a sponge could ever have. He's a starfish, and you'll usually find him clinging to the underside of a rock, doing what he likes best - sleeping and lying dormant. Patrick's not the brightest, even by starfish standards, but he's loyal - and he just loves SpongeBob. Together they make a great (but dangerous) pair.

BIG QUESTION 1: is Squidward bitter because he's an octopus called 'Squid'?

SpongeBob's neighbour is a surly octopus by the name of

Squidward Tentacles.

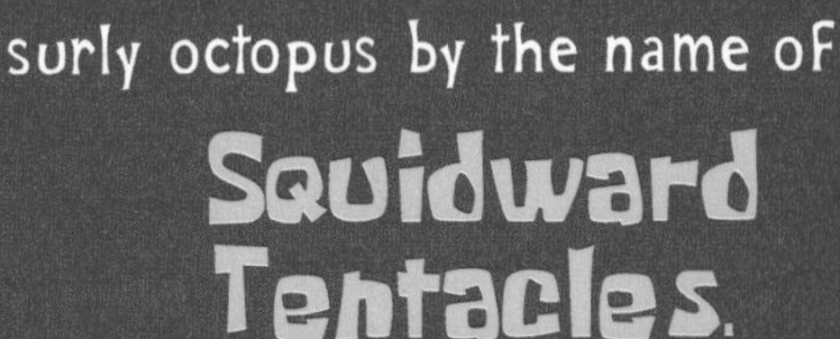

He's unusual in that everyone and everything annoys him. He thinks he's a great clarinet player, but the only person who agrees with him is SpongeBob - which is the only reason Squidward doesn't wash his tentacles of him.

Meet **Sandy Cheeks**, ace thrill-seeking, surfing, karate-kicking, weight-lifting super-squirrel. She lives, not in a tree, like any normal squirrel, but under the sea, thanks to a deep-sea diving suit and an air dome. SpongeBob is well and truly smitten with Sandy and hangs out with her as often as he can. Unfortunately, this can be dangerous, as being with Sandy usually means he needs to be wearing a hard hat.

The Krusty Krab has a rival in the form of Plankton's Chum Bucket. Plankton, the owner, is tiny, microscopic even, and has a bit of a complex about it. He's very noisy for his size and is always planning some evil plot to put the Krusty Krab out of business and steal Mr Krabs' famous recipe for Krabby Patties.

Mr Krabs is SpongeBob's boss at the Krusty Krab. Even though SpongeBob manages to annoy him almost all of the time, Mr Krabs can't help liking him. But what he likes even more than SpongeBob is money - and lots of it. in fact the only thing he likes better than money is his whale of a daughter, **Pearl**.

BIG QUESTION 2: if Mr Krabs eats a Krabby Patty, is he a cannibal?

Location, Location, Location
BIKINI BOTTOM
Bikini Bottom is an underwater city way down deep in the Pacific Ocean.
Bikini Bottom has Television. SpongeBob's favourite show is called MERMAID MAN AND BARNACLE BOY.
RULES of the ROAD
THERE'S EVIL AFOOT. E-E-VIL!
PAY ATTENTION, SPONGEBOB!
It has a Boating School run by Mrs Puff. She taught SpongeBob to drive a boat without any success at all.
12

Bikini Bottom even has its own ghostly pirate who haunts the town. He's called the **Flying Dutchman**.

The Krusty Krab is the fast food restaurant where SpongeBob Squarepants works as a cook. It's owned by his boss, Mr Krabs. It's a happening place where the Bikini Bottomers go to eat the house special, Krabby Patties.

Plankton's Chum Bucket is owned by (you guessed it) Plankton. It's the Krusty Krab's rival, but it's a no-contest situation really. Business isnt too good at the Bucket, very probably because SpongeBob isnt the cook there.

Plot: Paul Tibbet. Script, art, and lettering: Sherm Cohen. Coloring: Digital Chameleon. Special thanks to: Stephen Hillenburg and Derek Drymon.

GOOD MORNING, GARY! IT'S TIME FOR BREAKF- HIC! IT'S TIME FOR BREAKF- HIC!
IT'S TIME FOR BREAKF- HIC!
IT'S TIME FOR BREAKF- HIC!
HOW ABOUT SOME FOOD?
Gary

Meow?
DON'T WORRY-- IT'LL TAKE MORE THAN HICCUPS TO TRIP ME UP.
HIC!
OOPS! SORRY, PAL!
UM... I GOTTA GO TO WORK!
Gary

HIC!
Y'KNOW, SPONGEBOB--I'VE GOT A SUREFIRE CURE FOR THOSE HICCUPS!
HIC!
HIC

REALLY? YOU DO?
SURE! JUST TRY DUSTING MY LIVING ROOM SHELVES. WORKS FOR ME EVERY TIME!

GEE, THANKS, SQUIDWARD!
HEH, HEH... SUCKER!

HIC!
CRASH
HIC!
BOOM
HIC!
BASH

HIC!
OH, NO! SOB LOOK WHAT YOU DID TO GLASSY!
I'M SORRY, SQUIDWARD, BUT YOUR IDEA DIDN'T WORK! HIC! DO YOU HAVE ANY OTHER IDEAS?

YES! GO BOTHER PATRICK!
HIC!

AND SO...
THE BEST THING TO DO IS TO STAND ON YOUR TONGUE AND HOLD YOUR BREATH.
LIGE YITH?

HIC!

AW, TARTAR SAUCE! I'LL NEVER GET RID OF THESE HICCUPS!

OH! YOU HAVE THE HICCUPS?
WELL, HIC! WHAT DID YOU THINK I SAID?
I THOUGHT YOU SAID YOU HAVE THE HICCUPS.
I DO HAVE THE HIC! HICCUPS!
OH, WELL, THE BEST THING TO DO IS TO STAND ON YOUR TONGUE...
NEVER MIND!

WELL, YOU CAME TO THE RIGHT PLACE, SPONGEBOB!

HICCUP!
WE TEXANS HAVE A HICCUP CURE THAT GOES BACK TO THE DAYS OF THE ALAMO!

LEMME HAVE IT!
GLUG GLUG GLUG
HEY!

HIC!
THAT'S NOT THE HICCUP CURE, SPONGEBOB! THAT WAS MY LAUNDRY DETERGENT!

HIC!
THE KRUSTY KRAB
I HATE TO GO TO WORK IN THIS CONDITION, BUT MR KRABS IS COUNTING ON ME!
HIC!
HIC!
ENTER

BUT SOON...

WHAT'S TAKING SO LONG?

HURRY IT UP! I'M STARVING!

YOU CALL THIS A KRABBY PATTY?

HIC!

I WANT MY MONEY BACK!

SETTLE DOWN, YE SCURVY DOGS! IF THERE'S A PROBLEM IN ME RESTAURANT, I'LL SEE TO IT!

DID YOU STAND ON YOUR TONGUE?
YES!
DID YOU DUST SQUIDWARD'S SHELVES?
YES!
HOW ABOUT LAUNDRY DETER-GENT?
YES! YES!
HICCUP!
I'VE TRIED THEM ALL!

WELL, IT LOOKS LIKE THERE'S ONLY ONE THING LEFT TO DO...

YOU'LL HAVE TO TAKE A TRIP TO...
HICCUP ISLAND
"HICCUP HICCUP! ISLAND"?

NO! NOT "HICCUP HICCUP ISLAND," JUST "HICCUP ISLAND."
LOOK HERE.

EVER SINCE PHLEGMY McWELTERSON CAUSED THE WRECK OF THE S.S. GLOTTIS, IT'S BEEN THE CUSTOM OF THE SEA TO BANISH ALL HICCUPPING SAILORS TO THIS ISLAND OF LOST SOULS.
Hiccup!
Isle of the Hiccups

BUT I'M NOT A SAILOR, MR KRABS... I'M A FRY COOK!
AYE... THAT'S WHAT PHLEGMY McWELTERSON SAID, TOO.
C'MON, LAD... I'LL TAKE YOU THERE MYSELF.

LATER, OUT ON THE FAR END OF GOO LAGOON...
SO, WHAT DO PEOPLE DO ON HICCUP ISLAND?
WHAT DO YOU THINK? THEY HICCUP!
HIC! ANYTHING ELSE?
AYE, LAD... THEY CRY.
THEN THEY DRINK THEIR OWN TEARS AND CRY SOME MORE.
HIC!
HIC!
HIC!
HIC!
HIC!
HIC!
HIC!
HIC!
HIC!
HIC!
HIC!
HIC!
GULP! YOU'LL BE BACK FOR ME SOON, WON'T YOU, MR KRABS?
HIC!
SORRY, BOY... NO ONE EVER COMES BACK FROM HICCUP ISLAND.

IS THAT WHO I THINK IT IS?
AYE, IT'S THE FLYING DUTCHMAN.
BUT I THOUGHT HE HIC! LIVED IN DAVEY JONES'S LOCKER.
YES, BUT HE SUMMERS HERE ON HICCUP ISLAND.
AHOY, KRABS! I SEE YOU BROUGHT ANOTHER LOST SOUL TO WALLOW HERE IN ETERNAL MISERY!

AYE, DUTCHMAN. HE BE AFFLICTED WITH THE HICCUPS!
DID HE TRY STANDING ON HIS--
YES, YES! HE DID ALL THAT.

WELL, IF YOU THINK THIS WRETCHED DOG HAS WHAT IT TAKES, LET'S HEAR HIM HICCUP!
SOULS

GO ON, SPONGEBOB. HICCUP FOR THE FLYING DUTCHMAN.
...
WELL, I'M WAITING...

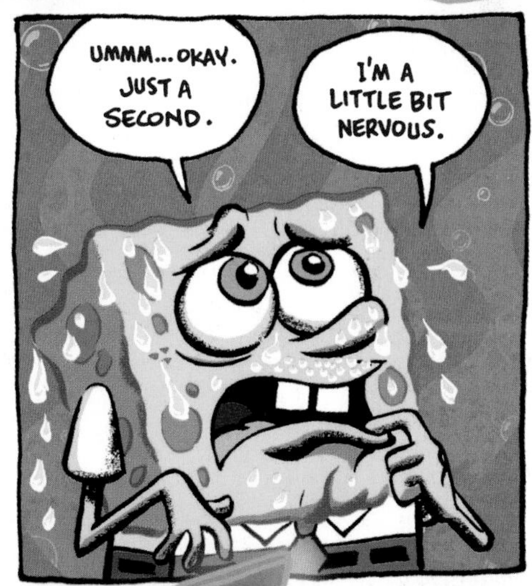
UMMM... OKAY. JUST A SECOND.
I'M A LITTLE BIT NERVOUS.

C'MON, LAD! YOU'RE MAKING ME LOOK BAD.
GULP! I'M SURE ONE'S COMING!
HURRY IT UP! I HAVEN'T GOT ALL DAY! I WANT TO HEAR YOU HICCUP, AND I WANT TO HEAR IT NOW!

Buh... buh...
I SAID HICCUP!
NOW!
WELL, YOU CAN'T COME TO HICCUP ISLAND. YOU CAN'T EVEN HICCUP!
NOW SCRAM!
I-I-I CAN'T DO IT! I'M SORRY!
BWAAAAAHH

IT'S A MIRACLE, SPONGEBOB! YOU'RE CURED!
DOES THAT MEAN WE CAN GO BACK NOW?

YIPPEE!
YES! RUN, BOY! LET'S GET BACK TO WORK!

IT WORKED! WE SCARED THE HICCUPS RIGHT OUT OF HIM!
THANKS, FLYING DUTCHMAN! I OWE YOU ONE!
I'VE GOTTA SAY, THAT'S A PRETTY CONTRIVED WAY TO CURE YOUR FRY COOK OF THE HICCUPS.
AYE-- MY METHOD MAY BE ELABORATE, BUT IT WORKS EVERY TIME! HA!
THIS SIDE UP
THIS SIDE UP
HIC!
HIC!
HIC!
HIC!
HIC!
HIC!
HIC!
Uh, oh.
Ye End

SpongeBob Loves ...

SpongeBob loves all these things - and more. Tick the loves you share with him, cross the ones you don't and draw something you love in the big bubble.

HI YA! OUCH!
i Love ...

How to Draw SpongeBob SquarePants

Draw SpongeBob SquarePants in the blank space by following these step-by-step instructions. Make sure you use a pencil with a good eraser, because some steps require erasing.

1

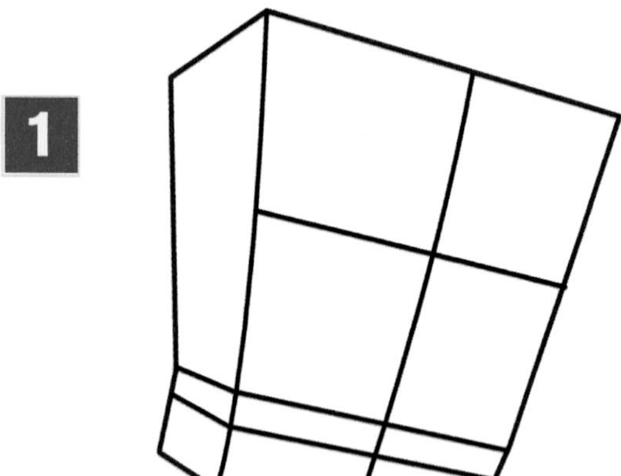

Start with a slightly wedge-shaped rectangle divided into sections.

4

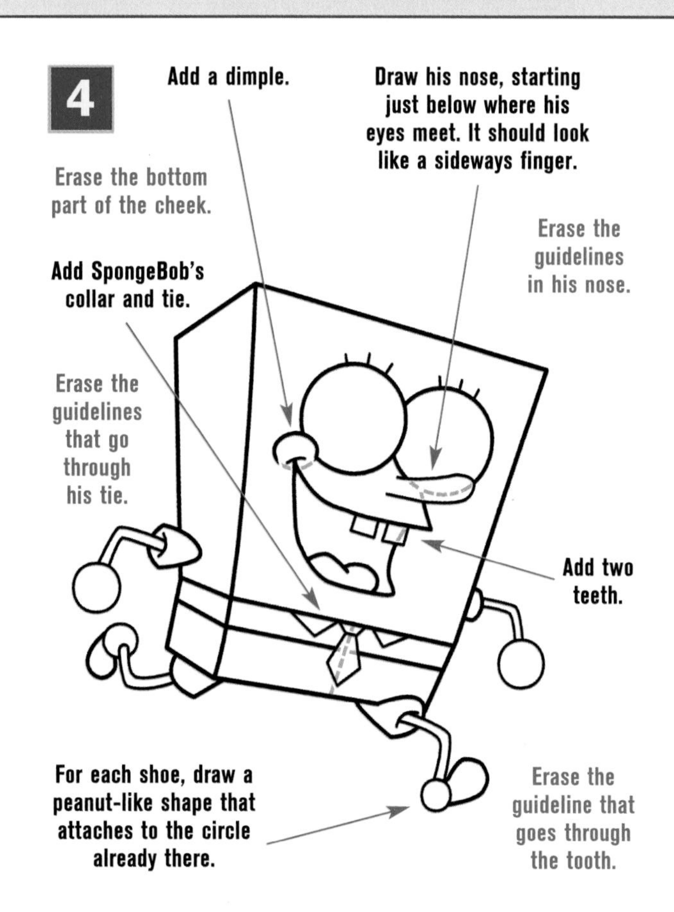

5

Illustration: Manuel Galán

2

Draw two circles resting on the centre lines. The left circle should slightly overlap the right circle.

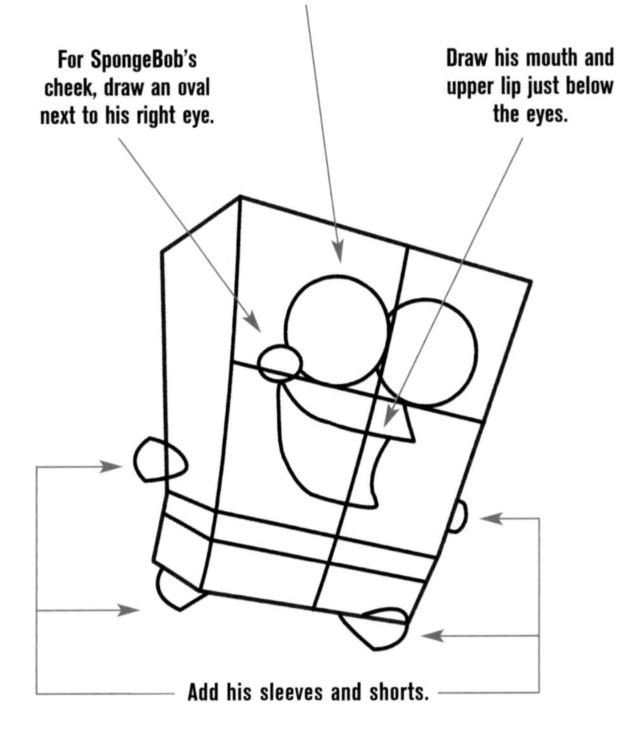

3

Draw his tongue inside his mouth.

Erase the guidelines inside the big rectangle.

Add eyelashes.

Add a curved line where his arm comes out of his sleeve.

Draw L-shaped tubes for arms and legs, then cap them with circles.

Erase the guidelines in his sleeve and shorts-leg.

Add a curved line where his leg comes out of his shorts.

6

Add holes to SpongeBob's surface.

Draw SpongeBob SquarePants here!

Story, art, and lettering: C.H. Greenblatt. Coloring: Digital Chameleon. *SpongeBob SquarePants* created by Stephen Hillenburg.

...HIS BEST FRIEND, PATRICK STAR!
IT'S A PERFECT COSTUME.
WHATEVER YOU SAY.
OKAY. SO IT PULLS IN THE GROIN.
SOON, THE SECRET OF THOSE HOT KRABBY PATTIES WILL BE MINE!
AND THEN I'LL RULE THE WORLD! AND I'LL BUY A BIG FOUR-WHEEL DRIVE, AND I'LL BE COOL!
GO, PLANKTON! IT'S YOUR BIRTHDAY! GO, PLANKTON! IT'S YOUR BIRTHDAY!

MOMENTS LATER...

OPEN UP! I COMMAND YOU TO OPEN THIS DOOR!
BINK BINK
BINK

WELL, A BIG HELLO TO--

AHEM!

OH! HEY, PATRICK!

YES, THAT'S RIGHT! I'M YOUR STUPID FRIEND, PATRICK!

LET'S GET GOING! THERE'S A BEAUTIFUL DAY OUT THERE JUST WAITING TO BE SMEARED WITH FUN!
KRABBY PATTY FORMULA, YOU'RE GOIN' DOWN!
Jellyfish Fields
WELL... HERE WE ARE... AT THIS PLACE.
OMIGOSH, PATRICK, LOOK! IT'S A--
RARE SOUTH SEAS ORANGE-THROATED JELLY!
VERY EXCITING. AND YOU KNOW WHAT ELSE IS EXCITING? THE KRABBY PATTY FORMULA! LET'S DISCUSS...
HMM... THAT'S WEIRD. IT'S MOVING IN AN ATTACK PATTERN.

BUT WE SHOULD BE OKAY. IT'S NOT AGGRESSIVE...

...TO ANYTHING BIGGER THAN A PLANKTON.

WOW! I'VE NEVER SEEN ONE THIS CLOSE!

ZAP

NEAT! THAT MUST BE THE VENOM SAC!

ZAP

I'VE READ THAT IT EVEN HAS STINGERS ON ITS STINGERS!

ZAP

HEY! NOW IT'S SLAPPING YOU! I DIDN'T KNOW IT COULD DO THAT!

ZAP

I THINK IT'S DONE. OH, WAIT...

ZAP

NOW IT'S DONE.

THAT WAS INCREDIBLE, PATRICK!

SINGING LOUD! SINGING LOUD! IF YOU MEAN IT, YOU GOTTA SCREAM IT!
SINGIN OUD! SINGING LOUD! IF YOU M A IT, YOU GOTTA SCREAM IT!

THE SECOND VERSE IS EVEN LOUDER! READY?
WHAT?

BLAST IT! I'VE GOT TO PRY THAT SECRET FROM HIM BEFORE MY EARDRUMS BURST!

FIST!

TEN VERSES LATER...
LET'S SEE... WHAT SHAPE SHOULD I BLOW THIS BUBBLE INTO, PATRICK?

HOW ABOUT THE SHAPE OF A SECRET FORMULA?

WAIT! I'VE GOT AN IDEA!

BLOW

IT'S A CINDER BLOCK!

CRUSH!
MY BACK!

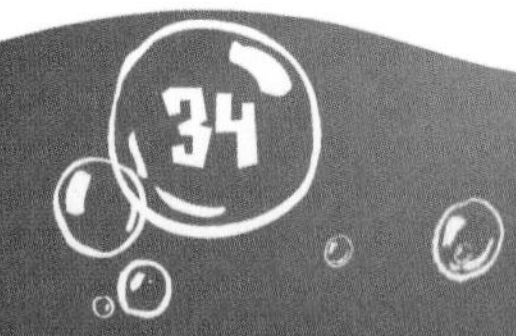

BEEP!
BEEP!
BEEP!
BEEP!

HEY, PATRICK! YOU KNOW WHAT TIME IT IS?
TIME TO TALK ABOUT THE SECRET FORMULA?

NO, SILLY. IT'S TIME FOR OUR DAILY "JOGGING IN PLACE" DRILL!

GET THOSE KNEES UP HIGHER!

HIGHER! THIS COULD SAVE YOUR LIFE, PATRICK! YOU NEVER KNOW WHEN YOU'LL HAVE TO JOG IN PLACE IN AN EMERGENCY!

HIGHER!

HIGHER!!

HIGHER!!!

TWITCH!
TWITCH!
TWITCH!

ALL RIGHT, THAT'S IT!!

ARE YOU OR ARE YOU NOT GOING TO TELL ME THE SECRET KRABBY PATTY FORMULA?!

THE SECRET FORMULA? WELL, OKAY.

IT'S REALLY SIMPLE. YOU JUST--
RUB RUB

HEY, SPONGEBOB!

WOW, LOOK! IT'S ME!

CURSE YOU ALL!

THAT WAS AWESOME, PATRICK! HOW'D YOU DO THAT?!
I'M JUST SPECIAL, I GUESS.

I'M SMALLER IN PERSON THAN I WOULD'VE THOUGHT.
YOU SURE ARE, BUDDY. YOU SURE ARE.
END!

Jellyfish Jam

by Steve Ryan

It's time for some jellyfishing! SpongeBob wants to max out his catch at Jellyfish Fields. Can you find the one path through the maze that allows SpongeBob to snag exactly 10 jellyfish?

Rules

- SpongeBob's net can only hold 10 jellyfish. He needs to reach **FINISH** with that amount – no more, no less.
- Whenever SpongeBob travels through a jellyfish space, the jellyfish is considered caught.
- SpongeBob can't travel over the same path twice.

START

FINISH

There's Only One SpongeBob
... or is there?
Can you find the one picture on this page that's an exact match for me ?

Puzzled Patrick

ANSWERS: 1. eyelashes are missing; 2. spot is missing; 3. eye colour; 4. tooth is missing; 5. arm is missing; 6. tie colour has changed; 7. shorts have changed colour 8. bike has changed colour

Home Sweet Home

In order to show up SpongeBob, Squidward built the fanciest pineapple house in Bikini Bottom. He started with a plain pineapple (N) and kept adding features. Can you figure out the correct sequence of additions? (By the way, the pineapple collapsed once Squidward opened the front door. He then moved back to his tiki head.)

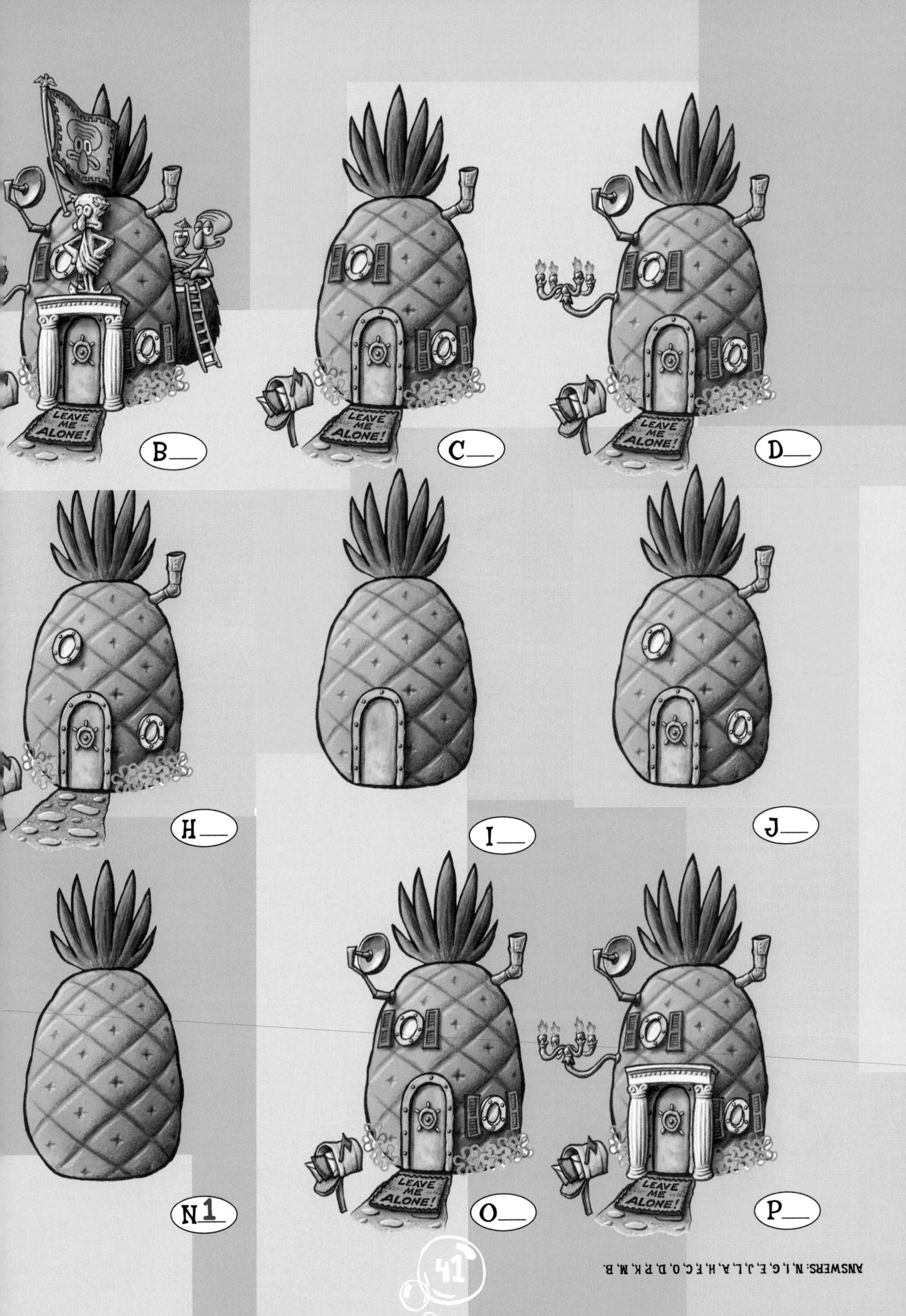

ANSWERS: N, I, G, E, J, L, A, H, F, C, O, D, P, K, M, B.

Pulling Faces With SpongeBob

If there's one thing SpongeBob likes better than chasing wild jellyfish and frying up Krabby Patties, it's pulling faces. Why not try some of his favourites? Get out a mirror or, better still, sit facing a friend and pull away. Why not take some photos of your best efforts and put them on the bulletin board on page 69?

YOU'RE LOOKIN' FINER 'AN BARK ON A TREE!
WHAT IS WRONG WITH YOU PEOPLE?

SPONGEBOB'S PET SNAIL, GARY

By the way, Gary, I love your new hat!

Story and art: James Kochalka. *SpongeBob Squarepants* created by Stephen Hillenburg.

SPONGEBOB'S PAL, Sandy Cheeks

Story: Sam Henderson. Pencils and inks: Vince Deporter. Coloring: Stu Chaifetz. *SpongeBob Squarepants* created by Stephen Hillenburg.

How to Make SpongeBob SquarePants

Here's what you'll need:

- a new standard-size yellow sponge (10 cm by 7.5 cm)
- 4 yellow pipe cleaners
- 1 white pipe cleaner
- red, black, and blue markers
- a long piece of red ribbon (or a sheet of red craft or construction paper)
- a sheet of brown craft paper
- a sheet of white paper
- two pencil-top erasers (any colour)
- plastic eyes from an arts-and-crafts store (optional)
- scissors
- glue
- ruler
- a grown-up to help

Ask a grown-up to help you make an action figure of your aquatic buddy with these step-by-step instructions.

1 LEGS

a. Cut two 9 cm-long pieces of yellow pipe cleaner.
b. Cut two 5 cm-long pieces of white pipe cleaner.
c. To make socks, wind each white pipe-cleaner piece around the bottom of each yellow pipe-cleaner leg.
d. Carefully poke each leg into the bottom of the sponge.

2 ARMS AND SLEEVES

a. Cut two 22.5 cm-long pieces of yellow pipe cleaner. Bend one end of each into four fingers.
b. For sleeves, cut two strips of white paper that measure 2.5 cm by 1.5 cm.
c. Roll each strip of paper into a tube, and glue each tube closed. Let dry.
d. Glue each sleeve onto the shoulder end of the arm, about 2.5 cm from the top. Let dry.
e. Poke the shoulder end of each arm into the sponge, about 4 cm up from the bottom of the sponge.

3 SHIRT AND SHORTS

a. Cut a strip of white paper that is 2.5 cm-wide and long enough to wrap around the sponge.
b. Cut a 1.5 cm-wide strip of brown craft paper the same length as the white strip.
c. Glue the brown strip to the bottom half of the white strip. Let dry.
d. Glue the brown-and-white strip to the sponge.
e. To make the legs of his shorts, cut two strips of brown paper that measure 2 cm by 2.5 cm.
f. Roll each strip of paper into a tube, then glue each tube closed. Let dry.
g. Glue the top of each tube to the top of each leg.

4 EYES, TIE AND BELT

a. Cut out two circles of white paper, each about 2.5 cm in diameter. Outline the edges with the black marker.
b. Glue the plastic eyes to the centre of each eyeball, or just draw in the eyes with the blue marker.
c. Glue the eyes onto the sponge so that SpongeBob's right eye slightly overlaps his left one.
d. To make the tie, cut out a small rectangle and a small diamond from the ribbon (or red craft paper). Glue them onto the centre of the shirt.
e. For the collar, draw a wide black V on either side of the top of the tie.
f. Draw dashes on the brown paper to make his belt.

5 FACE AND SHOES

a. With the black marker, draw three eyelashes above each eye.
b. Draw in the nose, mouth and two teeth.
c. Colour in the mouth with the red marker.
d. Colour both pencil-top erasers with the black marker. After they dry, slip one onto the bottom of each leg.
e. Bend each leg at the top of the eraser – and voilà! SpongeBob is ready for action.

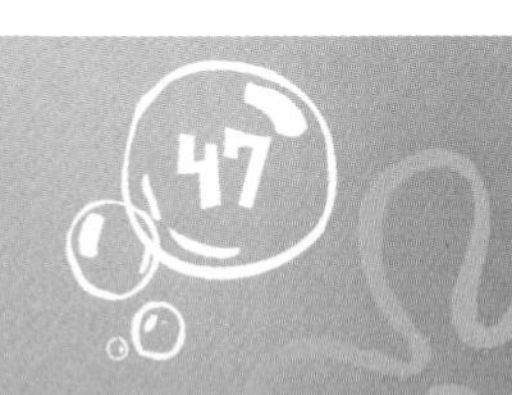

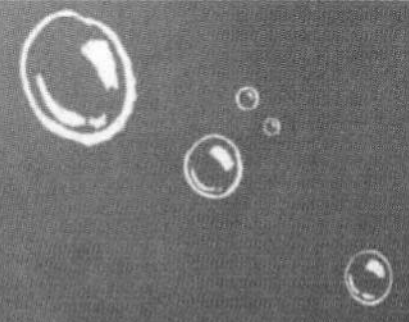

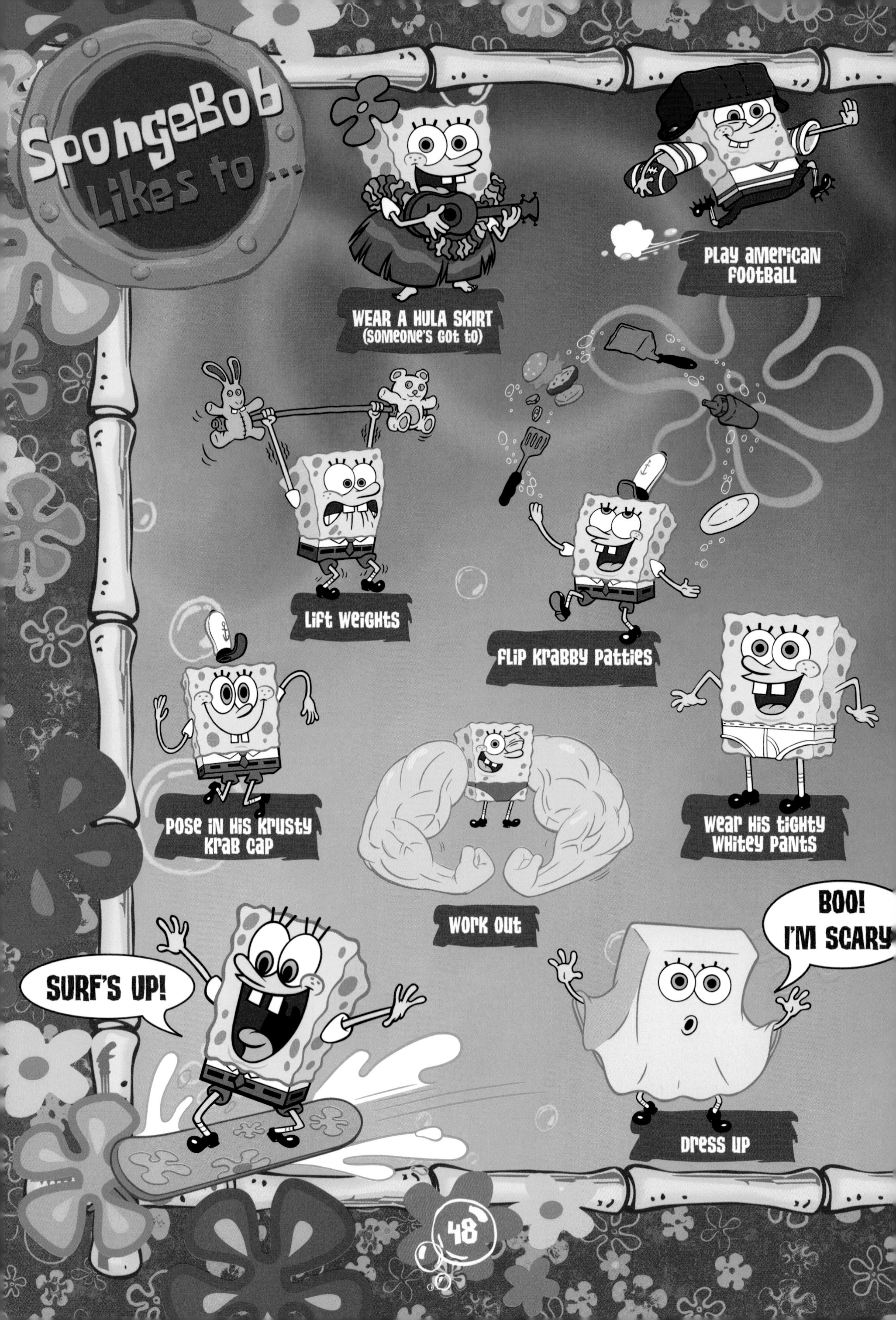
SpongeBob Likes to...
WEAR A HULA SKIRT
(SOMEONE'S GOT TO)
PLAY AMERICAN FOOTBALL
LIFT WEIGHTS
FLIP KRABBY PATTIES
POSE IN HIS KRUSTY KRAB CAP
WORK OUT
WEAR HIS TIGHTY WHITEY PANTS
SURF'S UP!
BOO! I'M SCARY
DRESS UP

I'M SPONGEBOB NUDIE PANTS!
GO WITHOUT PANTS
(SPONGEBOB NO PANTS)
GO JELLYFISHING
STRETCH
i like to...
Use this area to draw something you like doing.

Dancealonga SpongeBob
Join in the fun with SpongeBob and the gang. The Waddle 'n' Wiggle Waltz is easy to do if you follow the steps on the next page. Don't forget to waddle like a duck and wiggle your arms about. "i did it!" you'll shout!
OKEY DOKEY, THEN. WHICH WAY SHOULD I GO?
But first, can you help SpongeBob find which path leads to his dancing partner, Sandy?
1
2
3
4

NICKELODEON
SpongeBob SquarePants
House Party
SpongeBob's Waddle 'n' Wiggle Waltz
① Stand up straight –
Now jump: Good luck!
② Point your toes out wide
③ And waddle like a duck.
④ Point your toes front,
⑤ Put your hand on the ground.
Now keep it on the floor
While you walk around.
⑥ Time to stand up –
Feet together now.
⑦ Jump up high,
Cross those feet and land.
Wow!
⑧ Now hop back to normal
And then no more.
Time to wind things down:
Both feet on the floor.
⑨ Feet out, feet in –
One time, then again.
Now one more time!
You ask, "What then?"
⑩ Well, act like a nut!
Wiggle your arms about –
Shake your butt a bit,
"I did it," you'll shout!
There you have it.
And you can be sure
You've danced the best waltz
On the ocean floor!

SpongeBob SquarePants

"The Hole at the Bottom of the Sea"

Story, art, and lettering: Sherm Cohen. Coloring: Digital Chameleon. *SpongeBob SquarePants* created by Stephen Hillenburg. Special thanks to Stu Chaifetz.

...AND THIS IS DOWNTOWN BIKINI BOTTOM!
OH, HATTIE... I JUST CAN'T WAIT TO INTRODUCE YOU AROUND!
BUS
HI, LADY! MEET MY NEW FRIEND, HATTIE!
TAXI!
OKAY! WE'LL SEE YOU LATER!
HURRY, DRIVER!
YES, MA'AM!
VROOM
TAXI
WOW, HATTIE-- SHE WAS REALLY BLOWN AWAY!
WHA? OH, NO!
WHOOSH
SHE'S BLOWING AWAY! HATTIE! WAIT!
NO! NOT INTO THE WET PAINT!
NOT INTO THE CUTLERY SHOP!
CUTLERY
WET PAINT!
CHOMP! CHOMP!
NOT THROUGH THE HAT-EATING KELP!
OH, NO! NOT THE BOTTOMLESS PIT!
DANGER! BOTTOMLESS PIT AHEAD!

PATRICK! MY HAT!
HELP!

?
DONK!

PATRICK! YOU STOPPED MY HAT FROM FALLING INTO THE BOTTOMLESS PIT!

OH, SORRY.

HATTIE! COME BACK!
SPONGE-BOB!

COME BACK!

AAAAAAAAAAAAAAAAAAAA
LATER...
WHY DOES THIS KEEP HAPPENING?
AW, GEE, PAT--I'M SORRY I GOT YOU INTO THIS.
MUCH LATER...
HOW LONG DO YOU THINK IT'LL TAKE FOR US TO HIT THE BOTTOM?
IT'S CALLED "THE BOTTOMLESS PIT," PATRICK! IT DOESN'T HAVE A BOTTOM!!!
SO... HOW DOES IT GO TO THE BATHROOM?
LATER STILL...
ARE WE THERE YET?
I TOLD YOU, PATRICK... WE'RE GONNA BE FALLING LIKE THIS FOREV--
SHAVE
--OOF!
WHUMP
TOLD YA.
ALL RIGHT-- C'MON! I GOTTA FIND THAT HAT OR MR KRABS IS GONNA MOP THE FLOOR WITH MY HEAD!
AGAIN?
RUB RUB
HEY! TAKE A LOOK AT THIS!

IT LOOKS LIKE SOME KINDA LOST CIVILIZATION OF DEEP-SEA DWELLERS!
I SAW THAT MOVIE!
THERE'S MY HAT--AND A BUNCH OF OTHER JUNK THAT MUST'VE FALLEN DOWN THE PIT!

I'D LOVE TO STAY AND CHAT, BUT I'VE GOTTA GET MY HAT!
HA HA! NICE POEM, SPONGEBOB!

WOOP
WOOP

STOP! THIEF!
RUN!
DON'T LET THEM GET AWAY!

WE'RE ALMOST THERE!
BUT HOW'RE WE GONNA GET OUTTA HERE?
ERT!

WHEN YOU GET IN A JAM, YOU'VE GOTTA PUT ON THE OL' THINKING CAP!

PUFF PUFF

HANG ON, PAT!
WE'LL BE OUTTA HERE IN A JIF!

HEY, DO YOU THINK THOSE GUYS DOWN THERE CALL THIS "THE TOPLESS PIT"?
SIGH I DON'T KNOW, PATRICK. I JUST DON'T KNOW.

MANY BEARDS LATER...
LOOK, PAT! WE MADE IT! WE'RE BACK HOME!
GOOD-- 'CAUSE I'M GETTING HUNGRY!

BARNACLES! IT'S MR KRABS! I CAN'T LET HIM SEE ME OUT HERE WITH THIS HAT!
WE GOTTA LAY LOW TILL HE'S GONE!
SPONGEBOB...
SHH! WE GOTTA KEEP QUIET, PATRICK!

AAUGH! THEY GOT US! THEY'RE PULLING US DOWN!
HELLLP! HEEELLLL...

AND SO, BACK AT THE BOTTOM...
NO ONE ROBS FROM OUR SACRED SHRINE AND LIVES!
HOW DARE YOU STEAL ONE OF THE GIFTS FROM ABOVE!
NOW, STRANGERS-- FEEL THE WRATH OF OUR KING!
BUT, YOUR HIGHNESS... THAT'S NOT A HOLY RELIC! IT'S JUST MY HAT THAT FELL DOWN THE HOLE!
I KNOW NOT THIS WORD "HAT" THAT YOU SPEAK...
...BUT THIS SURE MAKES A NIFTY COVER FOR MY FAVORITE GOLF CLUB! I'M AFRAID I CAN'T LET YOU HAVE IT!

WE NEED THAT HAT, OR WE'LL BE STUCK DOWN HERE FOREVER!
YOU GOT ANYTHING WE MIGHT BE ABLE TO TRADE HIM FOR IT?

ALL'S I GOT IS MY LUCKY YO-YO.
GREAT! I'LL BUY YOU A NEW ONE WHEN WE GET BACK!

WELL, YOUR HIGHNESS... WHY SETTLE FOR A SIMPLE GOLF CLUB COVER WHEN YOU COULD TRADE IT FOR THIS SPLENDIFEROUS LUCKY YO-YO?
WHY, WITH THIS YO-YO, YOU CAN DO TRICKS LIKE THIS DOUBLE-INSIDE HOT-DOG FRENCH SWIRL! READY? WATCH!

THUD.

UH, NO THANKS...
...I'LL PASS.

WHY DO YOU CALL THAT YOUR "LUCKY" YO-YO?
'CAUSE I'M LUCKY IF I CAN GET IT TO DO ANYTHING!

NOW THERE'S ONLY ONE CHANCE LEFT... BUT I'VE GOT TO TRY IT!

AND SO...
SO LONG! GOOD LUCK!
TAKE CARE OF THAT NEW CROWN!

SNIFF! IT'S BEAUTIFUL! I'LL NEVER WASH MY SCALP AGAIN!

WELL, PATRICK... THAT WAS QUITE AN ADVENTURE... IT COST ME A GOOD PAIR OF UNDERPANTS, BUT I'M SURE GLAD WE MADE IT BACK HOME!

YIKES!
WE'RE GOING TOO HIGH!

DON'T WORRY--I'LL POP IT!
NO! PATRI--

BLAM
LOOK AT MY HAT! M-MAYBE I CAN (CHOKE) SEW IT BACK TOGETHER.
YOU WANNA BORROW MY NEEDLE?

AND SO, SPONGEBOB SETTLES IN FOR A LONG NIGHT OF HAT RECONSTRUCTION...
KNIT ONE, PURL TWO... OUCH!

THE NEXT DAY...
KRUSTY KRAB
IT TOOK ALL NIGHT, BUT HATTIE'S AS GOOD AS NEW... IF YOU DON'T LOOK TOO CLOSE!

WHAT'S WRONG, SPONGEBOB? YOU LOOK KINDA THREAD-BARE.
UGH... DON'T TALK ABOUT THREAD!
WHAT THE -- I DON'T BELIEVE IT!

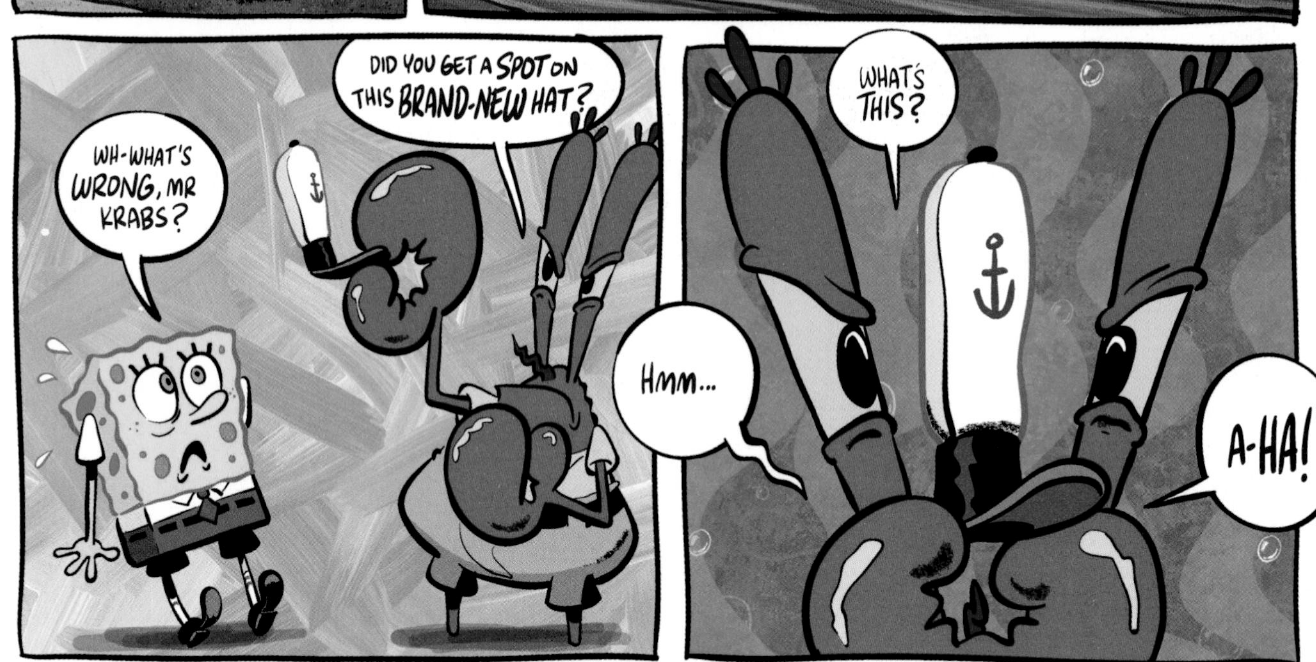
DID YOU GET A SPOT ON THIS BRAND-NEW HAT?
WH-WHAT'S WRONG, MR KRABS?
WHAT'S THIS?
HMM...
A-HA!

OH...IT WAS JUST A SHADOW. HERE YOU GO.
OK, YOU PASS INSPECTION!
TOK!
WHEW!
AAUGH! NO! MY HAT!
I'M SORRY, MR KRABS!
AW, QUIT YER BLUBBERIN,' BOY!
THERE'S PLENTY MORE WHERE THAT CAME FROM!
OF COURSE, I'M GONNA TAKE IT OUT OF YER NEXT FEW PAY-CHECKS!
OOOohhh...
end

Something Fishy

I THINK WE TOOK A WRONG TURN, PATRICK!
MAP

SpongeBob-mind

SpongeBob knows just about everything there is to know about Krabby Patties. They're his specialist quiz subject. In Fact, they're his ONLY quiz subject.

What's yours? SpongeBob? It is? Then pull up a big black leather chair, dim the lights and prepare to have your brain well and truly teased. Then check out your SpongeBob knowledge rating.

1. What Fruity kind of house does SpongeBob live in? ____________
2. Which town does SpongeBob live in? ____________
3. SpongeBob works as a cook at which Fast Food restaurant? ____________
4. What shape are SpongeBob's pants? ____________
5. Which squirrel is SpongeBob keen on? ____________
6. What is the name of SpongeBob's pet snail? ____________
7. What kind of creature is SpongeBob's neighbour Squidward Tentacles? ____________
8. Who is SpongeBob's best Friend and neighbour? ____________
9. What kind of Food does SpongeBob like to cook? ____________
10. Does SpongeBob's pet snail woof like a dog or meow like a cat? ____________

Score a point For each correct answer.

10 - wow
8-9 - great
6-7 - okay
4-5 - not good
2-3 - oh dear
0-1 - no comment

1 pineapple, 2 Bikini Bottom, 3 the Krusty Krab, 4 square, 5 Sandy Cheeks, 6 Gary, 7 octopus, 8 Patrick Star, 9 Krabby Patties, 10 meow like a cat.

BANG
Singalonga SpongeBob
Shout the SpongeBob song as loudly as you can, just like Painty the Pirate, and don't forget to flop around like a fish in the last verse.
Altogether now ...
ARE YOU READY, KIDS?
I CAN'T HEAR YOU!

CRASH
JELLYFISH JAM BAND
OOOHHH!
Who lives in a pineapple under the sea?
SpongeBob SquarePants!
Absorbent and YELLOW and POROUS is he!
SpongeBob SquarePants!
If nautical nonsense be something you wish,
SpongeBob SquarePants!
Then drop on the deck and flop like a fish!
SpongeBob SquarePants!
SpongeBob SquarePants!
SpongeBob SquarePants!
SpongeBob SquarePants!
HELLOOOOO BIKINI BOTTOM!

SpongeBob is Wild About...
ARRRGH!!!

YAHHHHHHOOOOOO!
NOTHIN' BUT NET!
Draw a picture of yourself in SpongeBob's frame, or attach a photo. Write your name on the line.
SpongeBob is wild about ... ______________________________

Bikini Bottom Bulletins

Here's a peek at the Krusty Krab's community bulletin board

Money of the Month Club

To Mr Krabs, my Biggest fan! Love, Ms Penny xoxoxo

February

IN CASE OF CHOKING

THIS MONTH'S K.K. SPECIAL

SUN	MON	TUES	WED	THURS
FREE BOTTOM BUN WITH PURCHASE				
2 of 3 TOP BUN!			6	7

LARRY LOBSTER'S ABS OF SHELL

GUARANTEED RESULTS IN JUST 5 WEEKS! ALSO ASK ABOUT "BUNS OF SHELL."

MODERN DANCE LESSONS!

taught by Squidward, "Master of the Dance"

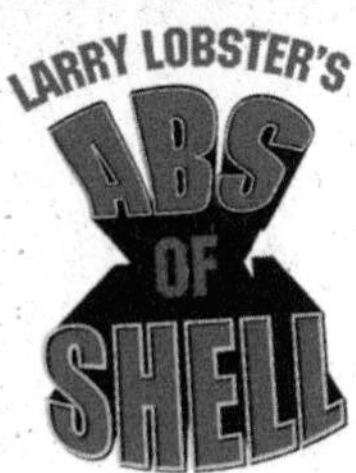

Only through the artistic endeavour of Interpretive Dance can one truly meld with the wonders of life majestic. -Squidward

Donate to the Bikini Bottom

CANNED FOOD DRIVE

No Canned Sardines, Please

Free clams to a good home! Ours just had 25,788,583 babies!

ROOMMATE WANTED:

Must be into karate, air and occasional hibernation. Warm-blooded critters a plus. Contact S. Cheeks at the Treedome.

555-6584 | 555-6584 | 555-6584

Grocery list:

- Milk
- DONUTS
- ice creem
- Tater Tots

Missing: Grocery list. has words on it. written by me. contact Patrick Star. really soon.

FAHLAOPO

"Fish Against Hooks, Lures, and Other Pointy Objects"

Meetings every Thursday, 8PM

The Amazing New Kon-Tiki X-5 JellyFishing Net!

Carbon-reinforced handle! Triple-stitched net! 2% more accurate! 6% faster swing time! 3% more aerodynamic! Guaranteed to catch .07% more jellyfish!

A MUST-HAVE FOR THE SERIOUS JELLYFISHERMAN!

Running over too many pedestrians? Can't tell a gas pedal from a flower petal? Come learn the fundamentals at

Mrs Puff's Boating School

— We'll teach all ages and all types (except sponges). —

by C. H. Greenbla

Use this board for your own bulletins, notices and pictures.